YOUR FAVOURITE
BEDTIME
STORIES
by Uncle Arthur

1

Illustrations by Annette Agard

ISBN 0-904748-70-7
5-vol. set 0-904748-75-8

Printed and published by
The Stanborough Press Ltd.
Alma Park, Grantham, Lincs., NG31 9SL
England

CONTENTS

How Ron rang the bells

Nobody living had ever heard the bells. In fact it was said that nobody had heard them for 400 years.

Some people wondered if there *were* any bells in the steeple at all!

Others said that the ropes had long since rotted away and that was why they were never rung.

Still others claimed that the bells would never ring again till someone in the church made some great sacrifice for God. Then, they said, the angels would ring them for joy!

That was a very lovely thought, and it brought many people to church with big expensive gifts, each one hoping that his gift would cause the bells to ring. Each Christmas Eve the building would be crowded as the King, the royal princes, the nobility, and all the businessmen of the city brought their offerings to lay on the altar.

But the bells never rang.

'Just an old story,' some whispered. 'They never will ring again.'

Living on the outskirts of this old Continental city were two young boys called Ron and Steve. They lived with their widowed mother in a small cottage. They were poor. Ron, the older brother, had to work hard to earn enough money to buy food for them all. Yet they were happy because Mother had brought them up to love God and find their greatest joy in helping others.

As Christmas drew near again, Ron tried hard to save a penny here and there so as to have something to spend on presents for Mother and Steve. More important still, he wanted to have something to put in the offering at the church on Christmas Eve. Everyone took something then, usually the best they could afford.

Of course, Ron and Steve had heard the story of the bells. Often they had stared up at the tall steeple and thought they could see them there, dull red with the rust of ages. Sometimes they wondered why someone did not tie new ropes to them and ring them again properly.

Now and then they talked to Mother about it.

'Do you think we shall ever hear the bells?' they asked.

'I don't know,' said Mother. 'I doubt it. I can't imagine that anybody would ever give anything so precious that they would make the angels ring those old bells again.'

Yet the boys, like many others, hoped on. Year after year they brought their gifts to church, just the same. Yet the bells did not ring.

Christmas Eve came once more. It was a wild and stormy night. There was deep snow on the ground and more was falling. Mother refused to go out and did not want the boys to go. But they pleaded, 'Do let's go, please! We've looked forward to this for so long. And the bells might ring tonight!'

At last Mother yielded, and the boys, their coats buttoned up tight around their necks, and their caps pulled down on their foreheads, set out for the church, Ron carrying his precious little offering inside his glove for safety.

It was a long, cold walk. Snow swirled around them. But their spirits were bright. All the way they talked about what they were going to see and hear. They had been looking forward to the Christmas Eve service all year. It was the one time they saw the King and the other big people in their beautiful robes. On this night, too, there was always wonderful music from the great organ and the white-robed choir. And there was always the chance that the bells might ring.

Suddenly as they trudged along, they heard a cry of distress. Peering through the driving snow they saw a man lying on the ground. His horse had slipped and thrown him, and he couldn't get up again.

'Help!' he called. 'Help!'

'What shall we do?' said Steve. 'If we stop to help him we shall be late for the service. And we'll never get in. It will be too crowded.'

'But we can't leave him alone out here,' said Ron. 'He might freeze to death.'

'But we'll be late. We'll miss everything.'

'I know,' said Ron. 'But the poor man needs help. You go on and I'll stay with him. Maybe I'll catch you up. Anyway, you can tell me all about it afterwards.'

Steve didn't like to leave his brother, but oh, how he

did want to go to that service! To miss seeing the King come was too great a sacrifice. He went on by himself.

But Ron stayed. He went over to the man and tried to help him up. But he was almost stiff with cold. Ron rubbed his arms and legs. Finally, with great effort, he helped him to his feet. By the time Ron had caught the horse and helped the man on to it again, it was late. So late, in fact, that he wondered whether it was worth while going to the church at all. But he went, happy that he had been able to help the man, but sad at the thought that he had missed the wonderful evening he had looked forward to for so long.

He reached the church door and opened it.

The place was packed. People were standing in the aisle. Everyone was looking eagerly towards the front. The minister had just asked for the gifts to be brought to the front. Ron pressed through the crowd to a place where he could see what was happening, so glad he had not missed anything.

The King rose to his feet.

What gift would he give this year? Money, jewels, deeds to land? No. Not this time. Suddenly a thrill passed through the whole mighty congregation as they saw him take the crown from his head and place it on the altar. 'Surely now', somebody whispered, 'the bells will ring!'

But no. Not a sound was heard. Only the rustling and whispering of the people.

Then the princes came forward and laid their gold

bars and gold plates and goblets beside the King's crown. Others followed with caskets of jewels. Still the bells did not ring.

Rich merchants followed, carrying sacks of gold and silver coins.

Then came the poorer people with the best gifts they could afford.

Yet the bells did not ring.

Now there was a long procession of people moving to the front and back again, each person laying something on the altar.

Ron, right at the back, was the last in the line. All the way down the aisle he wondered if the people knew he had come late. He had missed most of the service by helping that man. He felt that everybody was looking at him. And he had so little to give. Just a few pennies tucked in his glove.

Slowly he came nearer to the front. The people ahead of him presented their gifts and returned to their seats. Now he was last. All alone! And all eyes upon him!

He fumbled with his glove. Out came one penny, two, three, all of them. Timidly he stepped forward and placed them as near as he could, as near as he dared, to the King's beautiful crown.

Suddenly a strange sound was heard, coming from above.

Listen! What was it?

Bells!

Silence fell upon the mighty crowd.

Yes! It was the bells. They were ringing again at last!
From far up in the steeple they were filling the church
with wonderful music, unrolling out in glorious, tri-
umphant peals across the storm-swept city.

'Who is it?' cried the people. 'Who can have given
so great a gift?'

King, princes, commoners, rose to their feet and
looked around. But all they could see was a boy hurrying
down the aisle — a boy whose heart was throbbing with
a great happiness as he said to himself, 'What did *I* do
for God tonight?'

Don and the big dog

Most boys love dogs. But not Don. He was afraid of them. Just why, I do not know.

Perhaps one bit him when he was a baby. Anyway, the very sight of a dog made him want to run away from it.

As he grew older his fears grew less, but they never quite left him. Even when he was 10, 11 and 12, any big dog would awaken the old terror and have him looking for a place to hide.

One day while in church he heard the minister call for volunteers to go from house to house and collect money for foreign missions. 'Everybody can do something,' he said, 'fathers and mothers, young men and young women, boys and girls.'

Don's heart was touched, and he offered to do what he could. So he put his name down on the list of collectors, and a helpful lady told him where he could go and what he should say to the people. But she overlooked one thing: what to do about dogs.

To Don it seemed that every house had a dog, and every dog seemed to object to his knocking on the door. They growled and barked so much that he hardly made any calls at all. In fact, he passed far more houses than he visited.

He tried to tell himself that the dogs wouldn't do him

any harm, but that didn't do much good. Just seeing a dog on a drive or in a front garden was enough to send him next door.

Then he came to a fine-looking home standing some distance back from the road.

'These people will surely give a good gift,' Don told himself as he looked this way and that to make sure there was no dog on the premises. The coast seemed to be clear, so he walked smartly up the drive.

All went well until he was about two-thirds of the way to the house. Then he saw it.

It must have been the biggest dog in town. To Don it looked like a cross between a tiger and a rhinoceros. Slowly the great beast sauntered towards him.

Don froze in his tracks. For a moment he couldn't make himself go either forwards or backwards. Anxiously he glanced back at the entrance and he guessed that however fast he might run, he could never get there before the dog. In front of him he spotted a small gate into a patio beside the front door. He might just make that in time.

Scared, he leapt forward, reaching the patio a yard or so ahead of the dog. Slamming the gate behind him, and trembling from head to foot, he went up to the front door and rang the bell. There was no answer. He rang again. Then he knocked as loudly as he could with his knuckles. Still nobody came.

Meanwhile the great big dog paced up and down outside the gate, sniffing and snorting. Don was sure it

15

would tear him limb from limb if it got hold of him.

Time and again he prayed: 'Dear Lord, get me out of here! Please!' But still nothing happened.

Then he rang the bell again. This time, to his great relief, he heard footsteps inside. The door opened and a charming lady smiled down at him.

'Please, I'm — er — I mean I've — er — come from our church and — er — I'm — er — collecting money for foreign missions,' he stammered, shaking all over.

'What's the matter, dear?' asked the lady, smiling more broadly than before. 'Are you frightened of something?'

'It's the dog,' gasped Don. 'He chased me in here.'

'Oh, you don't need to be afraid of Judy,' said the lady. 'She's the gentlest pet you ever saw. She loves everybody and just wanted you to be friends with her.'

With that she opened the gate and let Judy into the patio. At once the dog went over to Don and licked his hand. As Don began to pat her she almost purred like a kitten, so pleased was she to be loved and noticed.

'Just a minute,' said the lady. 'I'll go and get something for your missions.' And she left Don to play with Judy!

When she came back she handed Don a £5 note.

'Thank you! Thank you very much!' he said politely, beginning to feel much better.

Judy went with him to the gate and he wasn't a bit afraid. Indeed, he seemed to lose his fear of dogs from that moment on. If a great big dog like that could be so gentle, why should he be scared of the smaller ones? Maybe they, too, were just waiting for him to be kind and friendly to them.

Myrtle the turtle

There was great excitement one day when Dad brought home a real live turtle. I don't mean one of those great big turtles you can see in a zoo, but a little teeny weeny one, not much more than three inches long, including its legs.

Small though it was, however, it was just like the big ones and had the funniest looking head you could imagine.

Little Minnie was so glad to have it that she laughed out loud for joy.

With Daddy's help she made a house for it in a glass tank, with some sand and rocks to make it look pretty and give the turtle somewhere to rest.

'There's just one thing you must remember,' said Dad. 'Little turtles don't like cold water. So when you put fresh water in the tank be sure it's warm.'

'I'll be very careful, Dad,' said Minnie. 'I want my turtle to live for a very long, long time.'

That brought up the question of what name should be given to the turtle — a boy's or a girl's?

'I really don't know,' said Dad.

'Then I'll call my turtle Myrtle,' said Minnie. 'That sounds good, "Myrtle the turtle". Don't you think so, Dad?'

'I do,' said Dad. 'A very good name indeed. Now

mind you look after it properly. And don't forget what I told you about the water.'

So Myrtle the turtle came to live with Minnie. But, alas, a few days later, when she went to look in the glass tank Myrtle seemed to be dead. It was the deadest looking turtle you ever saw.

Minnie was very upset. Tears began to run down her cheeks.

'I've something very sad to tell you,' she said to Dad as he came in from work. 'Myrtle is dead.'

'That's too bad,' said Dad. 'I'm very sorry.' Then he walked over to the glass tank and looked at the poor lifeless turtle.

'It's dead, I'm afraid,' said Dad.

Then he put his finger in the water.

'Oh!' he cried. 'It's hot! It's far too hot!'

'But you said I wasn't to let it be cold,' said Minnie.

'I know,' said Dad, 'but I didn't say so hot!'

Poor Minnie! Not till now had she realized that it was all her own fault. Running to her bedroom she fell on her knees beside her bed.

'Dear God,' she said, 'I'm so sorry I hurt poor Myrtle. I didn't mean to. I didn't know the water was too hot. Please, please, make her come alive again.'

Now you don't need to believe it if you don't want to, but some hours later, when Minnie looked into the glass tank, Myrtle the turtle was swimming about as usual.

No doubt it was a very tough turtle, and by this time

had got over the shock of the very hot water. As for Minnie, she danced with joy.

'Dad!' she cried. 'Come and see! God has made Myrtle come to life again!'

Just what really happened I shall never know, but to little Minnie it was a very precious experience which I am sure she will remember with thankfulness as long as she lives.

Susan's sacrifice

Susan loved horses. The biggest thrill she could think of was going to the local park and hiring a horse to ride.

This, of course, cost money. So Susan saved her pocket money from week to week until she had enough for another ride.

One day Dad gave her one of those saving boxes which opened by itself when you've put so much money into it. He said when the box opened she could use the money to ride her favourite horse 'Lady' at the park.

Susan was overjoyed, and began to save more carefully than ever. She offered to do all sorts of jobs in the garden, and around the house to get extra pennies so that her box would open sooner.

Well, one day, when her box was almost full, she went to church with her mother.

The preacher talked about the need for sending the Gospel of Jesus to those who've never heard about Him. He asked everyone to pray for somebody who had not heard about Jesus. Not only to pray for them, but to work for them by sending them missionary magazines to read week by week.

'Perhaps some of you would like to pray for five people,' he said, 'maybe ten or twenty, or even a hundred.'

Then he began to ask for people to put up their hands to show what they would be willing to do for God.

'Is anyone willing to pray and work for a hundred people?' he asked.

A hand went up. 'Thank you,' he said. 'That is wonderful. Now, will someone pray for twenty people?'

Several hands went up.

'How about ten? Who will pray for ten people?'

Many more hands were raised.

'And now five,' said the preacher. 'Who will pray for five?'

'I will,' said Susan, as her hand shot up.

Mother looked at her in surprise. She was glad that Susan understood what the preacher was saying and that her heart had been touched by the appeal. But she wondered whether Susan realized the cost of sending the missionary magazine to all those people.

'Did you stop to think how much money this will take?' she whispered.

'Yes,' said Susan. 'But it's all right, I must have enough in my box by now.'

Mother knew how hard Susan had been trying to save money and why she had been saving it.

'You are sure you don't mind?' she said to Susan as they left the church.

'I don't mind,' said Susan. 'I'm glad to do this for Jesus.'

It was a willing sacrifice she made and all heaven was made happier by it.

And because God will be no man's debtor, and gives back to us over and over again all that we give to Him

in love, something very wonderful soon happened.

One day the phone rang, and a man told Mother he was anxious to find someone who would be willing to look after one of his horses for a while. It was just like 'Lady', and perfectly safe for Susan to ride.

Mother was thrilled.

'Of course,' she said, 'we shall be glad to care for it for you. Susan will be delighted.'

Susan was, indeed. She said: 'You know, Mother, that day in church I had a hard time deciding to give my money to Jesus, but I put my hand up before I could change my mind. Now, see, instead of just hiring a horse now and then, He has given me one I can ride whenever I want to.'

Not every sacrifice is so quickly and wonderfully rewarded. But Jesus knows all about what we do for Him, and some day, in His own good time, He will give it all back to us, 'pressed down and running over'.

Dreamy Diana

'Time to get up, Diana,' called Mother from the bottom of the stairs. 'You'll be late for school.'

Diana grunted, turned over, murmuring: 'Yes, Mother,' and went on dreaming about her dolls and her beautiful doll's cot Daddy had promised to make her for next Christmas.

Five minutes passed. Then Mother called again.

'Diana, *will* you get up when I tell you? Please get up instantly or I shall have to come upstairs myself.'

This made Diana wake up suddenly and get on her feet, but she dreamed so much while she was dressing that she was late for breakfast, and that, of course, made her late for school.

Mother was very cross. It was not as if Diana had just done it this one day. It was every day. Every morning there was the same difficulty to get Diana out of bed, the same trouble to get her down to breakfast, and in fact, she seemed to be late for everything!

What could Mother do? 'Well,' she thought, 'I must do something or my little girl will grow up lazy.' So she thought of a plan.

Next morning Diana was called as usual, but again she did not get up. So Mother let her dream on, and went about the morning's work.

About ten o'clock a voice called from the top of the

25

stairs, 'I'm hungry, Mother. Can I have my breakfast now?'

'Breakfast?' exclaimed Mother in surprise. 'We cleared breakfast away hours ago. It's nearly lunchtime now.'

Diana began to cry. 'I want my breakfast!'

But Mother stood firm, as all mothers should, and told Diana that after this there would be just one time for breakfast and if little girls did not come when breakfast was ready, they wouldn't get any.

Well, the next morning, Diana forgot again, and again she lost her breakfast. However, she went to school almost on time.

Next morning Diana was late to breakfast again. She seemed to forget her lesson so quickly.

'What can I do?' said Mother to herself. Then she thought of another bright idea.

'Diana,' she said, 'you seem to be so tired in the morning I think you must go to bed earlier. After this you must go to bed when the baby goes.'

'But I'm not a baby,' said Diana.

'No,' said Mother, 'but you act like one in the mornings. In fact, the baby isn't half so sleepy as you are.'

So that night Diana was put to bed when the baby went, about half past six. Poor Diana! She cried herself to sleep, but next morning she woke up in good time and was the first member of the family down to breakfast.

Mother had at last discovered the secret! Diana was

not really lazy, only overtired. After that Diana was put to bed much earlier than she had been going before, and so long as she kept that up she never lost a single breakfast and was always early for school.

Clouds at a picnic

This story came to me from a girl called Geraldine who lives in Cuba in the West Indies. One day Geraldine came home and found her mother, a church school teacher, all hot and bothered. She had no money. Her school needed new desks, new books, new paint on the walls and lots of other things. Always when she told the school board about these needs she was met with the answer: 'No money.'

It was very discouraging. Sometimes Mother felt like giving up her job and letting someone else try to do it. 'It's no use,' she said. 'We can't go on like this. It isn't fair on the children.'

'Why don't we try to raise some money ourselves?' said Geraldine.

'Oh, we can't, we can't,' said Mother. 'That's been tried before.'

'Let *me* try,' said 12-year-old Geraldine. 'I'll plan a great big picnic with a sacred concert in the evening and invite lots of people. Then I'll sell the food to them, and you'll have the money you need for the school.'

'Thank you dear,' said Mother. 'That's very lovely of you. But think of the work. You couldn't do it. And I'm too busy to take on anything more just now.'

'Oh, I wouldn't try to do it all by myself,' said Geraldine. 'I'll get my friends to help me. You wouldn't have to do a thing.'

Geraldine was so sure she could do it, and that God would help her make the picnic a success, that Mother finally said she could do as she pleased.

So Geraldine told all her friends about the idea. They thought it was a very good one. They promised to bring food, and be there at the picnic grounds to help sell it.

After this good start Geraldine sent invitations to almost everybody in town and hoped all the people would come.

The day chosen for the picnic was the last Sunday in July. As it drew near, Geraldine became busier and busier getting everything ready. She didn't want anything to go wrong.

Then, on the Saturday morning, the weather changed. It began to rain. And it rained all the afternoon and evening. The picnic area was soaked — and so was everywhere else.

'It's too bad,' said Mother. 'I'm afraid you'll have to call it off. Nobody will come out in weather like this, and with the ground so wet.'

'I'm not going to call it off,' said Geraldine. 'Everything's going to be all right. I know it is. God gave me the idea for this picnic and He won't let it fail. I'm sure He won't.'

Sunday morning dawned bright and beautiful. The sun rose in a clear sky with all the promise of a perfect day.

Geraldine was delighted.

'I told you so, Mummy,' she cried. 'I knew it would be all right.'

Then she lit a fire outdoors and put a big pot on it in which she was going to cook the main part of the meal, the part she believed would bring the most money. Her spirits were high and even Mother felt more cheerful than usual. Then about ten o'clock the most awful-looking black cloud came up and blotted out the sun. A cold chill came over everything and everybody. People began to run for shelter.

'There's going to be a terrible storm,' said Mother. 'You'd better bring that pot indoors.'

'No, Mother,' said Geraldine. 'I'm going to leave the pot right where it is! I have faith to believe that no rain is going to fall today.'

'But can't you see the cloud?' said Mother. 'It's going to burst any minute.'

'I can see the cloud,' said Geraldine, 'but God is behind that cloud and He's not going to let it rain.'

(In her lovely letter, in which she tells me what happened next, Geraldine says that she suddenly thought of *Bedtime Stories* and all the children who asked Jesus to help in time of need. And then, while she watched that pot and cloud, she prayed and prayed that it might not rain.)

And it didn't rain. Instead, that big black cloud gradually moved away and the sun came out again.

Geraldine was delighted, and went on with her last preparations with a light and thankful heart.

30

But that cloud had done more damage than she knew. It had frightened everybody away. When the time came for the picnic to begin hardly anyone showed up.

It was heartbreaking. Geraldine could hardly keep back the tears.

All that food, and nobody to eat it!

'You shouldn't have got so much ready,' said Mother. 'I warned you that this might happen, with the weather as it is.'

'It's going to be all right,' said Geraldine, trying hard to keep up her faith. 'I'm sure it's going to be all right. If God took the cloud away He can bring the people after all, can't He?'

Gradually the afternoon wore away. A few people came, of course, but not nearly as many as Geraldine had planned for. By six o'clock half the food was still unsold.

Then came the sacred concert put on by Geraldine and her friends. They sang songs about Jesus and His love, and more and more people came slipping quietly into the seats to listen.

When it was all over somebody said, 'I'm hungry. Is there any food left?'

'Yes,' said Geraldine. 'There's plenty if you'd like some.'

And then it seemed that everybody was hungry at the same time, for they all made for the tables where the food was on display. In no time at all everything had disappeared. Nothing was left unsold.

So Mother got the money she needed for her church school, and Geraldine learned that faith cannot only move mountains, it can also sweep the darkest clouds clean out of the sky.

Nero the hero

Nero is a little black Dachshund with the heart of a lion.

Like most dogs he loves to chase other animals, but one day his fun got him into a lot of trouble.

When out in the forest with Kelvin his master, he spotted a fox, and the chase was on.

Then, suddenly the fox disappeared. He had found his hole — just in time.

But did this stop Nero? No indeed. He followed the fox inside.

On and on he went. Down and down. Round this corner and the next one.

Kelvin told Nero to come out, but he wouldn't. Probably he didn't hear his master's voice. He was so far in by now, and so far down.

Then something dreadful happened. Down there in the dark he took the wrong turning — as the fox no doubt hoped he would. All of a sudden poor Nero fell a long, long way. Then he found he could neither go forwards nor backwards. He was stuck!

Meanwhile Kelvin was getting more and more worried about his pet.

'Nero! Nero! Nero!' he called again and again. 'Good dog! Come back here! Come back!'

But Nero didn't come back. He couldn't.

Kelvin listened at the mouth of the hole. From far away came the sound of Nero's faint, desperate barking.

33

Now Kelvin was sure something had gone wrong. He ran to call his father.

Father came and listened. He became worried too.

'That dog is stuck down there,' he said. 'He can't get out. I'll go and get the bulldozer.'

While Kelvin waited at the hole Father ran to the farm and came back with the bulldozer and some pieces of pipe. Several of the neighbours came with him. They all loved Nero and wanted to do what they could to help rescue him.

Father started to clear off the top soil.

'Won't the earth fall in and cover him?' asked Kelvin.

'But we'll find the hole again,' said Father. 'It's my guess he's a long way down.'

Father was right. As the bulldozer bit into the ground they came across the hole zigzagging in all directions and could see what a wild chase Nero had had.

Then they came to the fork where Nero had made his mistake. Beyond it there was a hole almost straight down, getting narrower as it went.

'This must be it,' said Father. 'I reckon he's down there.'

He was.

Twenty feet down.

They could hear him again, only Nero wasn't barking any more. Now and again he gave a low growl, just enough to say he was still alive.

'Can't use the machine any more', said Father, 'or we'll suffocate him. Let's have the pipes.'

Gently the pipes were lowered, down and down, until the clear sound of Nero's growl made them realize that they were very close to him.

'What can we do now?' asked Kelvin anxiously.

'I don't know,' said Father. 'But at least the pipes will bring him air. And we'll pour some milk down to keep up his strength.'

Now somebody started to dig by hand, but soon gave up. The ground was too hard. 'It will take hours to get down that far,' he said. 'And the poor thing won't live that long.'

Night fell. Nero's growls ceased. Father decided that everybody might as well go home. They had done their best and, well, it was just too bad.

Poor Kelvin hated to leave the spot, but there was nothing else he could do.

In the morning he went back and poured some more milk down the pipe — just in case. But there was no sound from below now.

Kelvin found some wild flowers and made a funeral wreath and put it over the hole as a mark of his love.

Four days later there was a faint scratching on the door of Kelvin's home. Kelvin ran to open it. Outside was Nero. He looked a wreck. His eyes were sunk in his head, his ribs were sticking out from hunger, but his tail was still wagging feebly.

Somehow or other — nobody knows how — Nero had dug his way out of that hole, past his own funeral wreath, and made for home! What a dog! What a

35

lion-hearted dog! No wonder the whole village welcomed him back as a hero.

Nero was 'down' — but not out. He didn't know when he was beaten. Is there a lesson you and I can learn from him?

On the Queen's lap

Queen Elizabeth and her husband the Duke of Edinburgh travel all over the world. Wherever they go they try to meet as many people as possible.

At the beginning of her reign the Queen undertook a wonderful world tour. Many stories have been told about it. Perhaps the loveliest was about the little 4-year-old girl who wanted to sit on the Queen's lap. Some people blamed the little girl for what she did, but I don't. After all, she was only 4 years old, and if I were only 4 years old — who knows? — *I* might want to sit on the Queen's lap, too. She appeared to the little girl as the sweetest, kindest, gentlest Queen ever to sit on the royal throne since the dawn of history. Perhaps there are hundreds of thousands of little girls, even now, who would like to sit on her lap. Maybe some little boys too! Own up now, wouldn't *you*?

It happened in Brisbane, Australia. It was afternoon. Over 75,000 people had gathered for a children's rally to honour their beloved Queen. The sun was shining, flags were flying, bands were playing, and everybody was bubbling over with happiness.

Somewhere in the middle of that mighty crowd was little Narelle Dick, a bright, curly-haired girl of 4. Nobody had ever heard of her before, and certainly nobody had the slightest idea what was going on in her little head. But suddenly, as Narelle caught sight of the

Queen, with her beautiful, tender smile, she felt a great desire to go and give her a hug!

It never occurred to her that the big policemen wouldn't want a little girl to do anything like that, or that it might be rather trying for the Queen if 75,000 other children all tried to sit on her lap at the same time.

With but one idea in mind, she made her way to the platform where the Queen was sitting. Nobody took any notice of her as she pressed her way forward. Why should they? Who would worry about what a little 4-year-old might do?

Nearer and nearer to the Queen she came, and still nobody told her to go away. People sitting near the Queen gave Narelle a smile as she went by. Not one of them dreamed of what she was planning to do.

Then, when she was near enough, she suddenly jumped up on the Queen's lap and gave her a big hug. Surprised, the Queen smiled and said some kind words to her.

But the big people around were dreadfully shocked! 'Dear, dear, dear!' they said, 'what a dreadful child!'

Scotland Yard's Chief Inspector tried to pull Narelle away. She refused to let go! Finally he managed to detach her from the royal lap and, kicking and struggling, she was taken back to her *very* surprised mother.

What her mother said to her I do not know. I'm sure that all her life Narelle has cherished that blissful moment when she sat on the Queen's lap.

There *is* one royal Person who is glad to have boys and girls come to Him at any time! 'Let the little children come to me,' He says. 'Don't try to stop them. The kingdom of God is made up of such as these.' Luke 18:16.

'Come to me,' Jesus invites us all. When we answer His call there are no big policemen to tell us to go away. 'Anyone who comes to me', Jesus says, 'I will never turn away.' John 6:37.

Anyone, anywhere, any time who comes to Jesus is always, always, always accepted.

Pauline the baby deer

Don't ask me how a baby deer came to be called Pauline. I just don't know. Somebody must have given her the name and it stuck for the rest of her life.

The woodsman felling trees in the west of America saw her first when she was just a baby fawn. Her mother had been killed by a hunter, and there she was, all alone in the forest, with nowhere to go and nobody to care for her.

The woodsman brought her to the logging camp. Everybody fell in love with her at once. She was so little, so intelligent and so very affectionate.

Day by day Pauline was fed from a bottle until she was old enough to eat grass and leaves like grown-up deer. Being with people all the time she became more and more tame. In a little while she was just as much at home in the logging camp as if she belonged there.

Strangely, she loved to play with the dogs. And they didn't bite her or annoy her in any way. They just chased about together like old friends. As for children, she adored them. Once she wandered for miles, all around a big lake, looking for some boys and girls she knew.

When winter came, Pauline was taken down the mountain to a large farm. Here there were lots of dogs and many children. She loved them all, and they loved her. What a wonderful time they had together!

Often she followed the children to the little country school and peeped in the windows. If the door was open she walked in! You can imagine how much study was done then, or how much attention was paid to the teacher!

But Pauline was so good and quiet and friendly that nobody, not even Teacher, wanted to put her out!

By springtime Pauline had grown quite big, and now a great fear came into everybody's heart. Would she be shot like so many others of her kind when the hunting season began?

To make sure that hunters would recognize her as a tame animal the children tied a bright red ribbon and some big red handkerchiefs around her neck.

All went well for a time. During the hunting season the children could hear guns going off in the forest all around them. But dear Pauline, they felt certain, would be safe. Nobody would shoot her with all those red warning signals on her.

They did not know how cruel and heartless some people can be. On the very last day of the hunting season Pauline was shot by a woman hunter eager to bag her deer for the day. She didn't care about the red ribbon around Pauline's neck. She didn't care that the animal was tame.

But when Pauline died many people were sad. Some people were angry. But there was nothing anybody could do about it. They could only hope and pray for the day to come when there will be no more killing and

when, in God's beautiful kingdom of tomorrow, 'the wolf shall dwell with the lamb, and the leopard shall lie down with the kid; and the calf and the young lion and the fatling together; and a little child shall lead them'. When that day comes, 'They shall not hurt nor destroy in all my holy mountain, saith the Lord.' Isaiah 11:6,7; 65:25.

Helen's hairdo

Helen was a very lively little girl, full of fun and mischief, and just 5 years old.

One day two lovely twin girls, about 3 years old, came to live in the big house next door. They were very pretty children, with lots of blond curly hair, which was their father's pride and joy.

Helen's mother was anxious to make a good impression on the new neighbours and told Helen to be specially kind and friendly to the twins.

'Of course, Mummy!' said Helen. 'I think they're so sweet. I'll be ever so kind to them. Don't worry. I hope they come over to see me soon. Or shall I go over to see them first?'

'No, not until their mother invites you,' said Mother. 'I expect she's very busy getting the place tidy.'

'Then I 'spect they'll come here first,' said Helen.

'Maybe they will,' said Mother. 'But if they do and I am out, remember what I have told you.'

'Of course I will, Mummy. I'll be ever so kind to them.'

Helen was right. The twins did come first. Finding a hole in the fence, they came strolling into Helen's garden and made themselves quite at home.

Helen tried hard to be kind to them.

Then, just like girls, they all began talking about their hair.

'What lovely curls you both have!' said Helen. 'My mummy says they're even prettier than mine.'

'We don't like them,' said one of the twins. 'It hurts too much when our mummy combs them. We wish we had short hair, like boys.'

'Yes, we wish we *were* boys,' said the other twin. 'But Mummy says we can't change now.'

'Well, if you don't like your hair long, why don't you cut it off?' said Helen.

This was a new idea.

'How do you cut it off?' asked one of the twins.

'With scissors,' said Helen. 'Look, I'll show you.'

She got a pair of her mother's scissors and cut off a short piece of her own hair.

'Would you cut ours off?' asked the twins.

'If you want me to,' said Helen.

'Oh, do, please. Make us look like boys.'

Helen thought it was a wonderful idea. That would settle the question as to who had the prettier curls. So she made one of the twins sit on a low stool in the kitchen and started to work.

Snip! snip! snip! went the scissors, and one by one off came the curls. Pretty soon twin number one was looking as near like a boy as she ever would.

Helen was just starting on the other twin's hair when Mother returned. Horror-struck, she flopped into a chair while the twins, very scared, flew out of the back door and dashed home.

'Helen!' cried Mother. 'Whatever made you do it?

Whatever will their father say? He'll never forgive us.'

Just then there was a loud ringing of the front doorbell.

The twins' father was there already, red-faced and furious.

'Where's that little b-r-r-r-rat?' he demanded. 'How dare she cut off my little girl's beautiful curls!'

Then he caught sight of Helen, with tears pouring in rivers down her cheeks. 'You — you — you!' he began, but there was not much more he could say.

When he had gone, Helen tried to explain. But there could be no excuse for anything so dreadful, Mother said. She would have to be punished for her foolishness. But how? Then Mother had an idea.

'I think their father would feel better if you looked like a boy too,' she said.

'Oh, no, don't cut my curls off!' cried Helen.

'I'm afraid I'll have to,' said Mother. 'I hate to do it, but it's the only way to teach you a lesson you need to learn.'

So Helen had a hair-do too, just like the one she had given to one of the twins. Then there were two girls looking just like boys, one on one side of the fence and one on the other. By the time their hair had grown again — and it didn't take very long — they were both wiser and better children.

Rosie, the nasty, nose-biting rabbit

For Christmas Grandma had given Louise a number of crisp £5 notes in an envelope. And Louise knew *exactly* what she was going to buy with them.

She would buy a baby bunny-rabbit and a big, big hutch.

Grandma took Louise to a farm where baby rabbits were for sale. Louise was excited. There seemed to be hundreds of them! She stood among them wondering which to choose. They were all so cute and fluffy.

Just then Louise caught sight of Rosie. Rosie was a brown baby rabbit twice as frisky as all the rest. She was jumping about and, sometimes, all four paws were off the ground at the same time! Rosie even came and nuzzled Louise's shoes.

That did it.

'It's going to have to be this one,' Louise told the farmer. 'She's the liveliest. I shall call her Rosie.'

Grandma agreed.

Soon Louise was putting Rosie in a big hutch, with an even bigger run, in the back garden.

Lots of times every day Louise would sneak out and watch Rosie leaping about. She fed her, talked to her, played with her. Rosie was the most loved rabbit in town.

There was one thing that Louise would *not* do: clean Rosie out. This task fell to Mother.

So it was Mother who found out the *other* side to Rosie. Not only was Rosie the friskiest rabbit, she was also the naughtiest. Time and time again Rosie got angry and Mummy got scratched. Quite often it *really* hurt.

One day the family went on holiday. Rosie's hutch was placed on the back seat of the car and Louise sat beside it.

The family spent their holiday with Aunty in the country. Aunty had rabbits of her own. She also said she knew all about rabbits.

When Rosie was settled in her holiday quarters, Louise took Aunty out to see her. Aunty climbed into the pen and set about making friends with Rosie. She believed that if she rubbed noses with Rosie they would be friends for life.

Can you imagine what happened?

Just as Aunty lowered her nose to ground level Rosie sprang forward — and sank her long, Bugs-Bunny teeth into it!

Aunty didn't know whether to laugh or cry. For days she went around with a plaster on her nose. Ever after she called Rosie 'that nasty, nose-biting rabbit'.

Some time later, back home, Mummy came into the house in a bit of a hurry. Her legs were bleeding from Rosie's scratches. When she had applied something from the medicine cupboard, Mother sat down quietly by the side of Louise.

'Rosie is a bad, bad rabbit,' said Mother. 'We may

have to take her back to the rabbit farm and swap her for a better-behaved rabbit.'

Louise didn't like the sound of this and gave it some serious thought.

'Mummy,' she said, 'when we are bad does God swap us?'

This was a new idea to Mother.

'No,' she said. 'God loves us like the wonderful Father He is and when we are bad and ask forgiveness He forgives us.'

'Does God still love us when we're bad quite often?' asked Louise. 'Does God send us away?'

'No,' said Mother. 'To God we are always part of His great family. When we keep on being bad God keeps on loving us, hoping that His love will stop us wanting to be bad.'

'Then', said Louise, 'we should keep on loving Rosie.'

And that, as they say, was that.

At church shortly after, Louise learned a new song:

'Do you ever wonder
What God does
With naughty boys and girls?
He loves them.
Yes, He does.

'Do you ever wonder
What God does
With naughty Mums and Dads?
He loves them.
Yes, He does.'

So they kept on loving Rosie.

One day Mother said, 'Do you know something? Rosie has stopped scratching me! She really is quite a good rabbit now — *most* of the time.'

'That's it then,' said Louise. 'God's way even works with rabbits.'

And Rosie has continued to improve.

When Billy 'bashed' Bobbie

It was bedtime, and already Jimmy and Suzie, the two smallest children, were tucked between the sheets. It was Bobbie's turn to go, and lastly Billy's.

As the boys took off their clothes, had their baths, and put on their pyjamas, they said all sorts of teasing things to each other. Then Bobbie got into his bed, and Billy into his.

But not for long.

A moment later Billy was out of bed again, standing on Bobbie's bed, a pillow over his shoulder.

'I'm going to "bash" you,' he said.

'Oh, no, you're not,' said Bobbie, leaping to his feet and making a grab for his pillow.

He was too late.

Billy 'bashed' him hard. Bobbie fell heavily on the bed, but was up again in a moment, this time gripping one corner of his pillow in both hands.

Billy 'bashed' again, but missed, and now it was Bobbie's turn to 'bash'.

Soon the blows were falling fast and furiously, and the noise was terrible.

Of course Jimmy and Suzie couldn't sleep, and they rushed in to see what was going on.

Suddenly Billy gave Bobbie a great big 'bash' and

Bobbie lost his balance and fell on the floor. He tried to get up, but couldn't, and Bobbie got scared. So did Jimmy. He rushed downstairs shrieking 'Billy "bashed" Bobbie and he's crying. He can't get up.'

Mother rushed upstairs to find out what all the trouble was about. 'Are you hurt?' she cried, hurrying over to Bobbie.

'I don't know,' he said, 'I'm not sure.'

Quickly Mother tucked them all in bed and warned them not to get out again until the morning.

Later on she came in to see Bobbie. He was still wide awake and his bed was shaking. Mother asked him how he felt, but he couldn't answer properly. Mother was really worried now and told Daddy to call the doctor.

The doctor came in less than five minutes, and stayed until half past two in the morning. He came again at seven o'clock and at twelve o'clock, giving Bobbie some medicine and looking him all over.

He said he was afraid Bobbie would have to go away to hospital; but later in the day he agreed that if Bobbie could be kept very quiet for several days he might get better again at home.

For days and days Billy, Jimmy and Suzie crept around the house like mice, scared to make the tiniest noise.

Worrying over what he might have done to Bobbie, taught Billy a lesson he needed to learn. He never did any more 'bashing' after that.

Two greedy girls

This story is about two girls and their dog Trixie.

For a long time Pam and Paula had been begging Mum to let them make some toffee all by themselves. Now she had said, Yes. They could make it while she went to town shopping, provided the girls left the kitchen clean and tidy afterwards.

'Oh, goodie!' they cried, clapping their hands for joy. 'Don't worry, we'll leave everything just right.'

Of course they both thought they knew all about toffee-making — until they got started. Then they began to wish they had asked Mum a few more questions. How much sugar? What kind of sugar? What else should they put in? Which saucepan should they use? How long should they cook it for?

'I think we had better look at Mum's cookery book,' said Pam. So they found the cookery book and turned to the recipe marked 'Toffee'.

'Here it is,' cried Pam. 'Now you listen, Paula, while I read. "To make one pound of toffee take three-quarters of a pound of brown sugar, four-and-a-half ounces of butter, half a teaspoonful of water and half a lemon." Got that?'

'Yes,' said Paula. 'Go on.'

Pam continued: ' "Place the sugar in a saucepan with the butter, water, and part of the rind of the lemon. Boil till sufficiently done. Let it stand till boiling has ceased. Then stir in juice of lemon. To find out when toffee is done drop a little into a cup of cold water. Butter a shallow tin and pour in the toffee." '

'So now we know,' said Paula. 'Let's get started.'

They found the right sugar, weighed it carefully, and put it in the saucepan. Then they put in the butter and the water and waited for them to boil.

At what they thought was the right time they mixed in the lemon juice, poured the toffee into the buttered tin, and waited impatiently for it to cool.

Meanwhile Trixie was running about excitedly, licking up any grains of sugar that fell on the floor. 'Go away, Trixie!' cried Paula for the twentieth time. 'This toffee isn't for you!'

Trixie slunk into a corner.

'I think it's time we tried it,' said Pam.

'So do I,' said Paula. 'I can't wait any longer.'

So they took a knife and made the first cut.

'Looks a bit crystallized,' said Pam.

'It does,' said Paula. 'Did we boil it too long? Or not long enough?'

'I don't know,' said Pam.

'Anyway, it's lovely,' said Paula, tasting a piece.

Just then they caught sight of Mary Jane, the girl next door, coming up the drive with her mother.

'The neighbours!' groaned the two girls.

'Why did they have to come now?' said Pam.

'And what shall we do with our toffee?' asked Paula.

'Hide it!' cried Pam. 'Get it out of sight! Quickly!